# GRAHAM KENDRICK

## The Collection

*A Songs of Fellowship* Worship Resource

MAKE WAY MUSIC

KINGSWAY MUSIC
EASTBOURNE

United Kingdom:
CCL UK Ltd
PO Box 1339
Eastbourne
East Sussex
BN21 4YF

United States:
CCL Inc
6130 NE 78th Court
Suite C11
Portland
Oregon 97218

ISBN 0 86065 933 X

*Editor — Nigel Coltman*
*Arranger — Stuart Townend*

*Cover design by Julia Shearn, Greenleaf Communications Ltd.*

Thankyou Music
P.O. Box 75, Eastbourne BN23 6NW, UK.

Make Way Music
P.O. Box 683
Hailsham BN27 4ZB, UK.

North American distributors:
Kingsway Inc., c/o Alexandria House Inc
468 McNally Drive, Nashville, TN 37211.

Printed in Great Britain for
KINGSWAY MUSIC LTD
1 St Anne's Road, Eastbourne, E. Sussex BN21 3UN.

# *A Word From Graham......*

When the Samaritan woman at Jacob's well posed a question about worship to the Jewish stranger, the apparent simplicity of her words belied the multitude of divisive issues lurking behind them. Not only were there controversies concerning such things as holy places, traditions, priestly lineage and ceremonial procedures, but there were also centuries of religious and racial prejudice.

Jesus, without so much as a pause to comment on these external issues, spoke directly to the heart of the matter. The religious people were seeking, with much striving and argument, to determine who had the best location, tradition and liturgy, and who could claim the purest historical roots or the most impeccable doctrine; but Jesus announced what the *Father* was seeking. In the midst of our contemporary debates about forms, styles, traditions and differing interpretations of scriptural commands about worship, often the last question to be considered is what God might be looking for. Jesus declared: 'Believe me, woman, a time is coming when you will worship the Father neither on this mountain nor in Jerusalem......A time is coming and has now come when the true worshippers will worship the Father in spirit and truth, for they are the kind of worshippers the Father seeks. God is spirit, and his worshippers must worship in spirit and in truth' (John 4: 21-24). The measure of the true worshipper that the Father seeks is not the length of his historical tradition or the height of his hands above his head, but the depths of the love in his heart for the Father.

It is significant that the Samaritan woman's first act in her first few minutes as a 'true worshipper' was to gather her friends and neighbours, and breathlessly invite them to meet the person 'who told me everything I ever did'. The truth had set her free; the living water was beginning to well up within her, and she overflowed with the glories of Jesus. In the gathering momentum of these last awesome days, I believe that worship and the preaching of the Gospel are going to flow together as one powerful stream into the world, and the source of this powerful stream will be an ever deepening personal encounter, by the Spirit, with Jesus himself.

*Graham Kendrick*

# 1.

# All heaven waits

*Mt 6:10; Rom 8:34; Eph 4:4;*
*1 Thess 4:16–17; 2 Thess 2:8;*
*Heb 7:25*

Graham Kendrick & Chris Rolinson

Capo 5(Am)

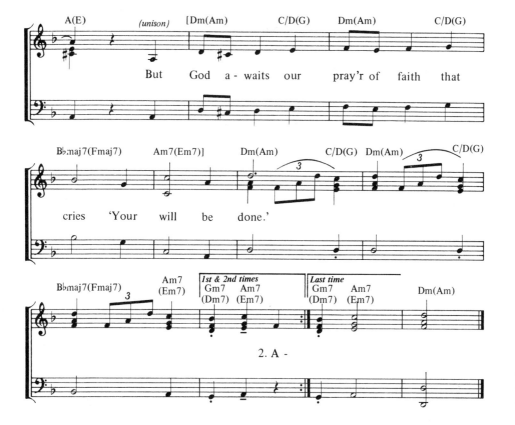

2. Awake, O church, arise and pray
   Complaining words discard.
   The Spirit comes to fill your mouth
   With truth, His mighty sword.
   Go place your feet on Satan's ground
   And there proclaim Christ's name,
   In step with heaven's armies march
   To conquer and to reign!

   *(Ladies)*
3. Now in our hearts and on our lips
   The word of faith is near,
   Let heaven's will on earth be done,
   Let heaven flow from here.
   *(Men)*
   Come blend your prayers with Jesus' own
   Before the Father's throne
   And as the incense clouds ascend
   God's holy fire rains down.

4. Soon comes the day when with a shout
   King Jesus shall appear
   And with Him all the church,
   From every age, shall fill the air.
   The brightness of His coming shall
   Consume the lawless one,
   As with a word the breath of God
   Tears down his rebel throne.

5. One body here, by heav'n inspired,
   We seek prophetic power;
   In Christ agreed, one heart and voice,
   To speak this day, this hour,
   In every place where chaos rules
   And evil forces brood;
   Let Jesus' voice speak like the roar
   Of a great multitude.

# 2.
# And He shall reign

Graham Kendrick

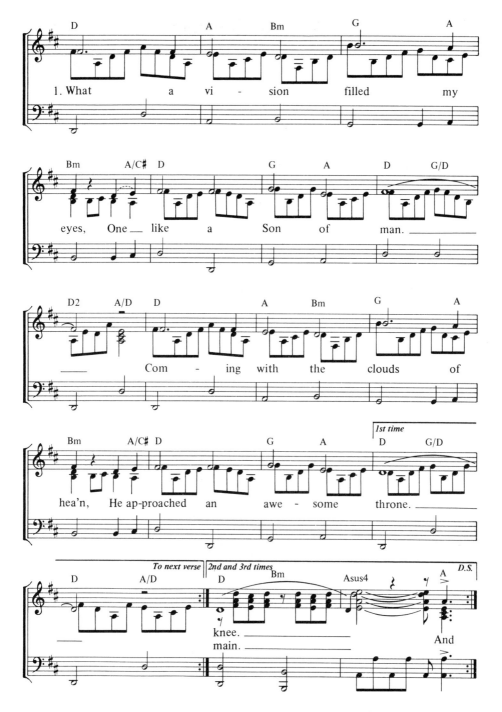

2. He was given sovereign power,
   Glory and authority.
   Every nation, tribe and tongue
   Worshipped Him on bended knee.

3. On the throne for ever,
   See the Lamb who once was slain.
   Wounds of sacrificial love
   Forever shall remain.

# 3.

# Come and see
## (We worship at Your feet)

Is 53:5–6; Mt 27:28–31; Mk 15:17–20;
Lk 22:63; 23:34; Jn 19:2, 5, 17;
2 Cor 5:21; Rev 5:12

Graham Kendrick

**Worshipfully**

1. Come and see, come and see, come and see the King of love; see the
pur-ple robe and crown of thorns He wears. Sol-diers
mock, ru-lers sneer as He lifts the cru-el cross; lone and
friend-less now, He climbs to-wards the hill. We
wor-ship at Your feet, where wrath and mer-cy meet, and a

2. Come and weep, come and mourn
   For your sin that pierced Him there;
   So much deeper than the wounds of thorn and nail.
   All our pride, all our greed,
   All our fallenness and shame;
   And the Lord has laid the punishment on Him.

3. Man of heaven, born to earth
   To restore us to Your heaven.
   Here we bow in awe beneath Your searching eyes.
   From Your tears comes our joy,
   From Your death our life shall spring;
   By Your resurrection power we shall rise.

# 4.

# Come now let us reason together

*Is 1:4-6, 16-20*

Graham Kendrick

mind is sick and our heart is faint with - in, _____ we are co - vered in brui - ses and sores and have no _ heal - ing. _____

D.C. al Coda

● CODA

snow. _____

2. So wash yourselves now,
   Take your evil deeds from My sight,
   Cease from evil and turn around
   To do what is right.
   Reproving the ruthless,
   Defending the helpless and poor;
   Where oppression has ruled
   The reign of justice restore.

3. Now if you consent and obey
   You'll eat from My hand
   But rebellion will bring a sword
   To your land.
   For those who forsake the Lord
   Shall be brought to an end,
   But righteousness comes to redeem
   Those who turn again.

# 5. Come see the beauty of the Lord

*Ps 27:4; Is 53:6; Mt 27:29;
Mk 15:17; Jn 19:2; Rev 5:12*

Graham Kendrick

*Thoughtfully, building throughout\**

1. Come see the beau-ty of — the Lord,

come see the beau-ty of — His face.

See the Lamb that once was slain, see on His palms is carv'd your —

name. See how our pain has pierc'd His heart,

and on His brow He bears— our pride; _____

a crown of thorns. _____

Come see the beau-ty of __ the Lord,

come see the beau-ty of __ His face. _____

*This song is sung as a call and response throughout, the congregation copying the leader or the ladies following the men.*

2. But only love pours from His heart
As silently He takes the blame.
He has my name upon His lips,
My condemnation falls on Him.
This love is marvellous to me,
His sacrifice has set me free
And now I live.

# 6. Darkness like a shroud (Arise shine!)

Capo 4 (C)

Ps 119:105; Is 60:1–3;
Mt 5:14; Jn 8:12;
Eph 6:10, 17; Rev 21:23

Subdued, becoming bright

Graham Kendrick

1. Dark - ness like a shroud cov - ers the earth.

Ev - il like a cloud cov - ers the peo - ple. But the

Lord will rise up - on ___ you and His glo - ry will ap - pear on you,

na - tions will come ___ to your light. ___ A -

rise, shine, your light has come, the glo - ry of the Lord has ris'n on you. A -

2. Children of the light,
   Be clean and pure.
   Rise, you sleepers,
   Christ will shine on you.
   Take the Spirit's flashing two-edged sword
   And with faith declare God's mighty word;
   Stand up and in His strength be strong.

3. Here among us now
   Christ the Light
   Kindles brighter flames
   In our trembling hearts.
   Living Word, our lamp, come guide our feet
   As we walk as one in light and peace till
   Justice and truth shine like the sun.

4. Like a city bright
   So let us blaze;
   Lights in every street
   Turning night to day.
   And the darkness shall not overcome
   Till the fullness of Christ's kingdom comes,
   Dawning to God's eternal day.

# 7.
## Do you not believe it?
### (A new thing)

Capo 3(C)

*Is 43:19-21*

Graham Kendrick

Do you not be-lieve it? ____ Can you not per-ceive it? I do a
Will you not be-lieve it? ____ Will you not re-ceive it? I do a

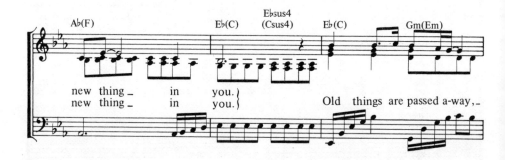

new thing _ in you.)
new thing _ in you.)
Old things are passed a-way, _

all things are new, let Me do a new _ thing ___ in

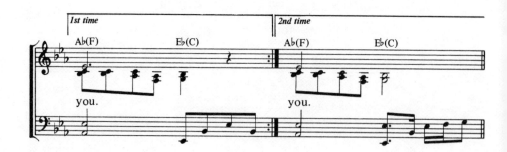

*1st time*
you.

*2nd time*
you.

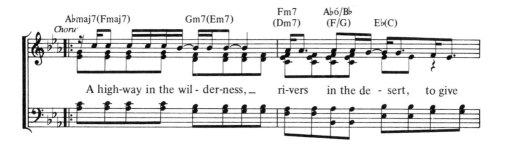

A high-way in the wil - der-ness, __ ri-vers in the de - sert, to give

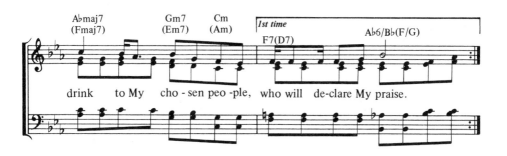

drink to My cho - sen peo -ple, who will de-clare My praise.

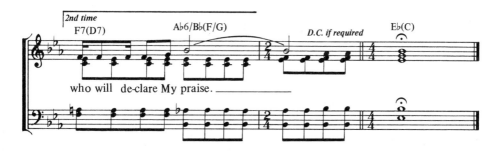

who will de-clare My praise. _____

# 8.  Father God we worship You

*Jn 4:23*

Graham Kendrick

2. Jesus King, we worship You,
   Help us listen now to You.
   As You move among us now
   We worship You.

3. Spirit pure, we worship You,
   With Your fire our zeal renew.
   As You move among us now
   We worship You.

# 9. Father, never was love so near
## (Thanks be to God)

Graham Kendrick

2. Jesus, the heart of God revealed,
   With us, feeling the pain we feel.
   Cut to the heart,
   Wounded for me,
   Taking the blame,
   Making me clean.

# 10.

# For this purpose

Rom 6:9; 1 Pet 2:24; 1 Jn 3:8;
Rev 12:10–11

Capo 2(C)

Graham Kendrick

*Flowing*
*Intro.*

1. For this pur - pose Christ was re-veal'd to de - stroy all the works of the Ev - il One. Christ in us has ov - er - come, — so with glad-ness we sing — and wel-come His king- dom in.

2. In the name of Jesus we stand,
By the power of His blood
We now claim this ground.
Satan has no authority here,
Powers of darkness must flee,
For Christ has the victory.

## 11.
# For Zion's sake
## (Royal diadem)

*Is 62:1-3*

Graham Kendrick

1. For Zion's sake I will not keep si - lent, for Jer-u-sa-lem I will not keep qui - et, till her right-eousness goes forth like brightness, like a flam-ing torch her sal-va-tion. _____ You will be a crown of beauty in the hand of the Lord, _____ you will be a roy-al di-a-dem in the

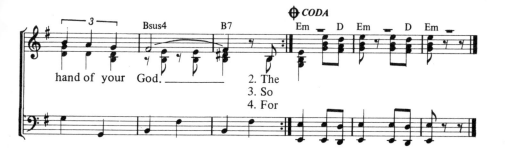

hand of your God.

2. The
3. So
4. For

2. The nations will see your righteousness,
   And all kings will see your glory,
   And you will be called by a new name
   Which the mouth of the Lord will choose.

3. So take no rest for yourselves,
   All you who remind the Lord,
   And give Him no rest until He makes
   Jerusalem a praise in the earth.

4. *As verse 1.*

# 12.

# From heaven You came
## (The Servant King)

*Is 53:11; Mt 20:28; 26:39;
Mk 10:45; 14:36; Lk 22:42;
Jn 20:27; Rom 12:1;
Eph 6:7; Phil 2:7*

Capo 3(C)

Graham Kendrick

1. From heav'n You came, help-less babe, en-ter'd our world, Your glo - ry veil'd; not to be served but to serve, and give Your life that we might live. This is our God, _____ the Ser - vant

2. There in the garden
Of tears,
My heavy load
He chose to bear;
His heart with sorrow
Was torn,
'Yet not my will
But Yours,' He said.

3. Come see His hands
And His feet,
The scars that speak
Of sacrifice,
Hands that flung stars
Into space
To cruel nails
Surrendered.

4. So let us learn
How to serve,
And in our lives
Enthrone Him;
Each other's needs
To prefer,
For it is Christ
We're serving.

# 13.

## From the sun's rising

Ps 113:1–3; Mt 9:37–38; 28:18–20; Lk 10:2

Capo 2 (C)

Steadily

*Verse*

Graham Kendrick

From the sun's ri-sing un - to the sun's set-ting, Je-sus our Lord shall be great in the earth; and all earth's king-doms shall be His dom-in-ion, all of cre-a-tion shall sing of His worth.

*Chorus*

Let ev-ery heart, ev-ery voice, ev-ery tongue join with spi - rits a-blaze; one in His love, we will cir-cle the world with the song of His

praise. O, let all His peo-ple re - joice, ___ and let all the earth ___ hear His

voice! ___ voice! ___ Let all His peo-ple re -

joice, ___ and let all the earth hear His voice! ___

2. To every tongue, tribe
   And nation He sends us,
   To make disciples
   To teach and baptise.
   For all authority
   To Him is given;
   Now as His witnesses
   We shall arise.

3. Come let us join with
   The church from all nations,
   Cross every border,
   Throw wide every door;
   Workers with Him
   As He gathers His harvest,
   Till earth's far corners
   Our Saviour adore.

# 14.

# God is good

Ps 100:5

Graham Kendrick

**Fast and rhythmic**

God is good, we sing and shout it, God is good, we cel-e-brate.

*To Coda*

God is good, no more we doubt it, God is good, we know it's

true. And when I think of His love for me my heart fills with praise and I

feel like danc-ing. For in His heart there is room for me and I run with arms op-en'd

*D.C. al Coda*

wide. _____

*CODA*

*(Shout)*

we know it's true. Hey!

# 15.  Hear, O Lord, our cry

## (Revive us again)

Ps 85:6

With strength

Graham Kendrick

2.  Hear, O Lord, our cry,
    Revive us, revive us again.
    For the sake of the children
    Revive us, revive us again.
    Lord, hear our cry.
    Lord, hear our cry.

# 16.
## Hear the sound of people singing
### (The Christmas child)

Graham Kendrick

**Gently, but with expectation**

Lyrics:

1. {Hear the sound of peo - ple
   In the streets the lights are

sing - ing, _____ all the bells are ring - ing _____ for the Christ-mas
glow - ing, _____ but there is no know - ing _____ of the Christ-mas

Child. _____ }
Child. _____ }

Oh, _____ let this Child be born in your heart,

oh, _____ let this Child be born in your heart, _

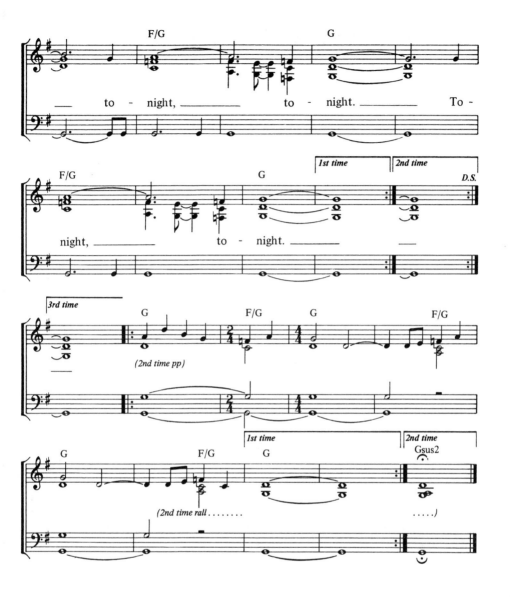

2. Will our wars go on forever,
And will peace be never
At Christmastime?
If we keep Him in the manger
Then there is no danger
From the Christmas Child.

# 17. Here in this holy place

*Heb 10;19-22;*
*Mt 17:5; Lk 10:38-42*

Graham Kendrick

1. Here in this ho - ly place, be - yond the veil, Your awe - some pre - sence bids us si - lent now. In ho - ly fear we stand, feel - ing the breath of Your Spi - rit blow - ing here.

2. Cleansed by the precious blood,
   Now we draw near
   In full assurance
   Of Your perfect love.
   Boldly we come before
   Your throne of grace,
   For Your Spirit calls us here.

3. Dear Lord I want to hear
   Your gentle voice,
   Let other voices
   Cease their worrying.
   And in the stillness
   Open my eyes
   To Your lovely smiling face.

——————— ◆◆◆ ———————

*Heaven is my throne*
*and the earth is my footstool.*
*Where is the house you will build for*
*me?*
*Where will my resting place be?*
*Has not my hand made all these things,*
*and so they came into being?*

ISAIAH 66:1–2

——————— ◆◆◆ ———————

# 18.

# He that is in us

Phil 2:9; 1 Jn 4:4; Rev 17:14

Capo 2 (C)

Graham Kendrick

**Joyfully**
*Chorus*

2. All the powers of death and hell and sin
Lie crushed beneath His feet.
Jesus owns the Name above all names,
Crowned with honour and majesty.

# 19.
# He walked where I walk
## (God with us)

Is 7:14; Mt 1:23; Heb 4:15

Graham Kendrick

Quite quick, with a steady rhythm

1. (Leader) He walked where I___ walk, (All) (He walked where I___ walk.)
   (He knows my frail - ty, (He knows my frail - ty.)

(Leader) He stood where I___ stand, (All) (He stood where I___ stand,)
shared my hu - ma - ni - ty, (shared my hu - ma - ni - ty,)

(Leader) He felt what I___ feel, (All) (He felt what I___ feel,)
tempt - ed in ev - 'ry way, (tempt - ed in ev - 'ry way,)

|  | (Leader) | (All) |
|---|---|---|
| 2. | One of a hated race, | (echo) |
|  | Stung by the prejudice, | (echo) |
|  | Suff'ring injustice, | (echo) |
|  | Yet He forgives. | (echo) |
|  | Wept for my wasted years, | (echo) |
|  | Paid for my wickedness, | (echo) |
|  | He died in my place, | (echo) |
|  | That I might live. | (echo) |

# 20.    If My people, who bear My name    *2 Chron 7:14*

Capo 4(Am)

Graham Kendrick

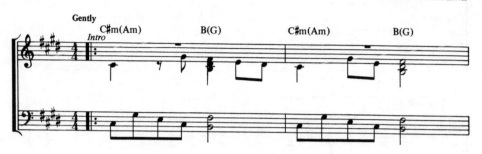

If My peo - ple, who bear My __ name, will

hum - ble them-selves and pray; if they seek My __

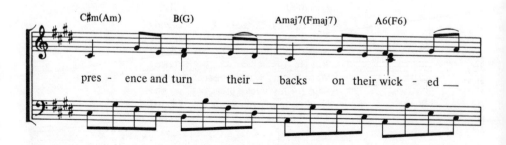

pres - ence and turn their __ backs on their wick - ed __

# 21. Immanuel

Is 7:14; 9:6; 53:3, 5, 7; Mt 1:23; 11:19; Lk 7:34

Graham Kendrick

Im-man - u - el, ___ God is with ___ us, ___

Im-man - u - el, ___ He is here.

Im-man - u - el, ___ He is a - mong ___ us, ___

Im-man - u - el, ___ His king-dom is here.

1. Won-der-ful Coun-sell - or, they laughed at his

2. He was despised and rejected,
   A man of sorrows acquainted with grief.
   From Him we turned and hid our faces;
   He was despised, Him we did not esteem.

3. But He was wounded for our transgressions,
   He was bruised for our iniquities.
   On Him was the punishment that made us whole,
   And by His stripes we are healed.

4. He was oppressed, He was afflicted,
   And yet He opened not His mouth.
   Like a lamb that is led to the slaughter,
   Like a sheep before his shearers He did not speak.

*Suggested order: Chorus, v.1, v.2, chorus, v.3, v.4, chorus.*

# 22.     Immanuel, O Immanuel

*Is 7:14; 53:5;*
*Mt 1:23; Heb 4:15*

Graham Kendrick

*O Lord, our Lord,*
*how majestic is your name in all*
*the earth!*
*You have set your glory*
*above the heavens.*

PSALM 8:1

# 23.

# I'm special

*Jn 3:16; 15:15*

Capo 2(C)

**With feeling**

Graham Kendrick

I'm spe - cial be - cause God has lov'd me, for He gave the best thing that He had to save me; His own Son Je - sus, cru - ci - fied to take the blame, for all the bad things I have done.

# 24.

# I want to be a history maker
## (History makers)

*Mt 6:10; Lk 11:2; Rom 7:4; Eph 1:4; 5:18*

Graham Kendrick

1. I want to be a his-tory ma-ker, (I want to be a his-tory ma-ker) I want to be a world _ sha-ker, (I want to be a world _ sha-ker) to be a pen on his-tory's pa-ges, (to be a pen on his-tory's pa-ges) faith-ful to the end of the a-ges. (faith-ful to the end of the a-ges)

*Chorus* I want to see Your king-dom come,

2. I believe I was called and chosen (*echo*)
   Long before the world's creation, (*echo*)
   Called to be a holy person, (*echo*)
   Called to bear good fruit for heaven. (*echo*)

3. We want to be the generation (*echo*)
   Taking the news to every nation, (*echo*)
   Filled with the Spirit without measure, (*echo*)
   Working for a heavenly treasure. (*echo*)

# 25.  I will build My church

*Mt 16:18*

Graham Kendrick

# 26. I worship You, O Lamb of God

Capo 2(D)

Graham Kendrick

Worshipfully ♩ = 52

1. I wor-ship You,_ (I wor-ship You,_) O Lamb of God, who takes a-way_ (who takes a-way_) the sin _ of the_world. I world. Al - le - lu - ia, al - le - lu - ia, al - le - lu - ia, al - le - lu - ia. 2. I -ia.

2. I kneel before the Lamb of God . . . (etc.)

# 27.

# Jesus is King

*Phil 2:9-11; Eph 1:20-23; 1 Cor 15:24*

Capo 2(C)

Graham Kendrick

1. Je - sus is King seat-ed high o - ver all, and the name that He bears is the King of kings and Lord of lords at whose mighty pow'r ev'-ry knee shall bow ___ ___ and ev' - ry tongue con-fess that Je - sus Christ is ___ Lord, He is Lord.

2. Jesus our King by the cross overcame,
Now the whole hosts of darkness are under His feet.
Now we are in Christ and His victory is ours
And in Him we reign, we shall see His kingdom come
For Jesus Christ is Lord, He is Lord.

# 28.     Jesus put this song into our hearts     *Ps 30:11; Eph 2:14*

Capo 5 (Am)                                                      Graham Kendrick

'Hebrew' style, getting faster

1. Je - sus put this song in - to our hearts, ___
Je - sus put this song in-to our hearts, ___ it's a song of joy no one can
take a - way, ___ Je-sus put this song ___ in-to our
hearts. ___

2. Jesus taught us how to live in harmony,
   Jesus taught us how to live in harmony,
   Different faces, different races, He made us one,
   Jesus taught us how to live in harmony.

3. Jesus taught us how to be a family,
   Jesus taught us how to be a family,
   Loving one another with the love that He gives,
   Jesus taught us how to be a family.

4. Jesus turned our sorrow into dancing,
   Jesus turned our sorrow into dancing,
   Changed our tears of sadness into rivers of joy,
   Jesus turned our sorrow into a dance.

5. *Instrumental.*

# 29.     Jesus, stand among us

*Mt 18:20; 26:26; Mk 14:22;*
*Lk 22:19; 1 Cor 11:23–24;*
*Eph 2:13; 4:15–16*

Capo 3 (C)

Graham Kendrick

2. So to You we're gathering
Out of each and every land,
Christ the love between us
At the joining of our hands;
O, Jesus, we love You . . . (*etc.*)

*(Optional verse for communion)*

3. Jesus stand among us
At the breaking of the bread,
Join us as one body
As we worship You, our Head.
O, Jesus, we love You . . . (*etc.*)

# 30.

# Led like a lamb
## (You're alive)

Is 53:7; Mt 28:6, 18; Mk 16:6;
Lk 24:6; Jn 20:16; 21:14

Graham Kendrick

1. Led like a lamb to the slaugh-ter in si-lence and shame, there on Your back You _ car-ried a world of vio-lence and pain.

Bleeding, — dy-ing, — bleeding, —

*For the antiphonal Alleluias the congregation divide into three parts.

2. At break of dawn, poor Mary,
   Still weeping she came,
   When through her grief she heard Your voice
   Now speaking her name.
   Mary, Master, Mary, Master.

3. At the right hand of the Father
   Now seated on high
   You have begun Your eternal reign
   Of justice and joy.
   Glory, glory, glory, glory.

# 31.
# Let it be to me

Graham Kendrick

**Gently flowing**

Let it be to me ac - cord-ing to Your word. Let it be to me ac - cord-ing to Your word. I am Your ser-vant, no rights shall I de - mand. Let it be to me, let it be to me, let it be to me ac - cord-ing to Your word.

———————— ♦♦♦ ————————

*Clap your hands, all you nations;*
*shout to God with cries of joy.*
*How awesome is the Lord Most High,*
*the great King over all the earth!*

PSALM 47:1–2

———————— ♦♦♦ ————————

# 32. Lift up your heads
## (O you gates)

*Ps 24:7; Eph 1:20–21*

Strongly

Graham Kendrick

1. Lift up your heads O you gates, swing wide you ev - er - last - ing doors.

*1st time* Lift up your

*2nd time* doors.

*Chorus* That the King of glo - ry may come in, ___ that the King of glo - ry may come in. ___ That the King of glo - ry

2. Up from the dead He ascends,
   Through every rank of heavenly power.
   Let heaven prepare the highest place,
   Throw wide the everlasting doors:

3. With trumpet blast and shouts of joy,
   All heaven greets the risen King.
   With angel choirs come line the way,
   Throw wide the gates and welcome Him:

# 33.
# Like a candle flame
## (The candle song)

Graham Kendrick

**Softly, with awe**

1. Like a can-dle flame, flick-'ring small in our dark-ness. Un-cre-a-ted light shines through in-fant eyes.

*Chorus*

(Men) God is with us, al-le-lu-ia, (Women) God is with us,

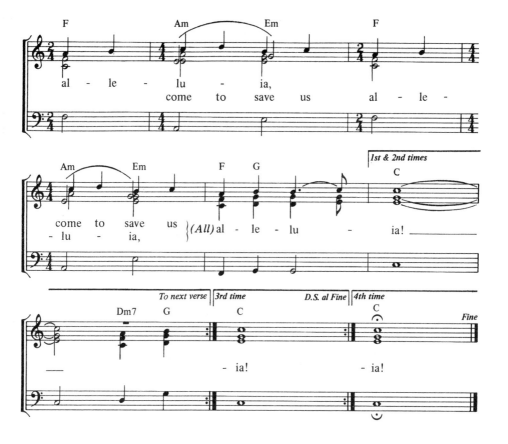

al - le - lu - ia, come to save us al - le -
come to save us (All) al - le - lu - ia!
- lu - ia, - ia! - ia!

2. Stars and angels sing,
   Yet the earth
   Sleeps in shadows;
   Can this tiny spark
   Set a world on fire?

3. Yet His light shall shine
   From our lives,
   Spirit blazing,
   As we touch the flame
   Of His holy fire.

# 34. Look to the skies

*Lk 2:8-14; Is 9:6-7;*
*Thess 4:16-17; Rev 22:3-5*

Capo 3(D)

**Triumphantly**

Graham Kendrick

1 Look to the skies, there's a cel - e - bra - tion, lift up your heads, join the an - gel song, for our Cre - a - tor be - comes our Sav - iour, as a ba - by born. An-gels a-mazed bow in a - do - ra - tion, glo - ry to God in the high - est heaven, send the good news out to ev - 'ry na - tion for our hope has

2. Wonderful Counsellor, Mighty God,
   Father for ever, the Prince of Peace.
   There'll be no end to Your rule of justice,
   For it shall increase.
   Light of Your face
   Come to pierce our darkness,
   Joy of Your heart come to chase our gloom.
   Star of the morning, a new day dawning,
   Make our hearts Your home.

3. Quietly He came as a helpless baby,
   One day in power He will come again.
   Swift through the skies He will burst with splendour
   On the earth to reign.
   Jesus I bow
   At Your manger lowly,
   Now in my life let Your will be done.
   Live in my flesh by Your Spirit Holy
   Till Your kingdom comes.

——————  ♦♦♦  ——————

O Lord, open my lips,
   and my mouth will declare your
      praise.
You do not delight in sacrifice, or I
      would bring it;
   you do not take pleasure in burnt
      offerings.
The sacrifices of God are a broken
      spirit;
   a broken and contrite heart,
   O God, you will not despise.

PSALM 51:15–17

——————  ♦♦♦  ——————

# 35.
# Lord, have mercy

*2 Chron 7:14*

Graham Kendrick

# 36.

# Lord, have mercy
# on this nation

Graham Kendrick

Lord, have mer - cy on this na - tion, for the sake of Je - sus Christ.

# 37.

# Lord make us still
## (May the peace)

Ps 46:10; Eph 4:16; Phil 4:7;
1 Pet 5:14; 2 Cor 13:14

Graham Kendrick

Gently

1. Lord make us still in Your pre-sence, list - 'ning for Your whis-per in our hearts. Come, Ho-ly Je - sus, a - mong us; of Your bo-dy each of us a part. May the peace of Christ be with

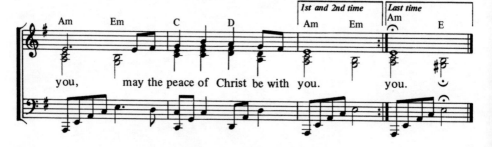

you, may the peace of Christ be with you. you.

2. As we reach out to each other
   May our hands be Yours to touch and heal.
   Lord come and touch my *brother/sister,*
   Make *him/her* know that You are all *he/she* needs.

3. Now may the love of the Father
   Keep you resting in His warm embrace,
   And may the Holy Spirit
   Send you out with power and with grace.

*How lovely is your dwelling-place,*
*O Lord Almighty!*
*My soul yearns, even faints*
*for the courts of the Lord;*
*my heart and my flesh cry out*
*for the living God.*

PSALM 84:1–2

# 38.

## Lord, the light of Your love
### (Shine, Jesus, shine)

Capo 2(G)

*Ps 139:23; Jn 1:5; 8:12, 32; 2 Cor 3:18; Rev 22:1*

Graham Kendrick

2. Lord, I come to Your awesome presence,
   From the shadows into Your radiance;
   By the blood I may enter Your brightness,
   Search me, try me, consume all my darkness.
   Shine on me, shine on me.

3. As we gaze on Your kingly brightness
   So our faces display Your likeness,
   Ever changing from glory to glory,
   Mirrored here may our lives tell Your story.
   Shine on me, shine on me.

# 39.

# Lord, we come
## (Join our hearts)

*Ps 133*

Graham Kendrick

**Gently**

*Verse*

1. Lord, we come in Your name, gathered here to worship You. Join us all in harmony, Spirit come. *(Men)* So And And

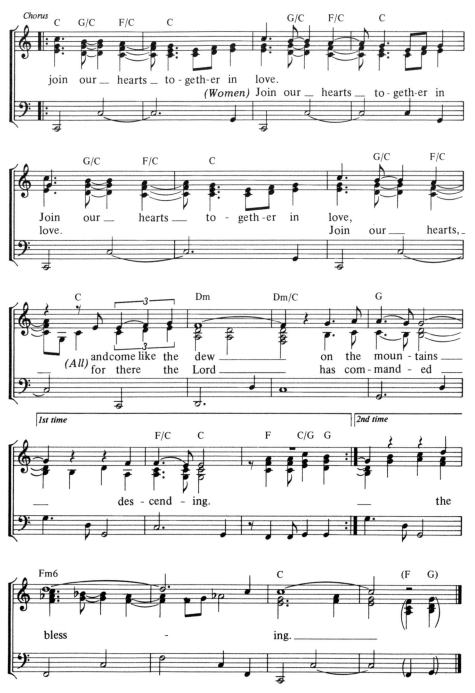

2. O how good, how beautiful, *(Women)*
When we live in unity;
Flowing like anointing oil *(Men)*
On Jesus' head.

3. So let us all agree
To make strong our bonds of peace.
Here is life forever more,
Spirit, come.

# 40. Lord, You are so precious to me

*1 Jn 4:19*

Capo 2 (G)

Graham Kendrick

2. Lord, You are so gracious to me,
Lord, You are so gracious to me
And I love You,
Yes, I love You
Because You first loved me.

*Sing to the Lord a new song;*
*sing to the Lord, all the earth.*
*Sing to the Lord, praise his name;*
*proclaim his salvation day after*
*day.*
*Declare his glory among the nations,*
*his marvellous deeds among all*
*peoples.*

PSALM 96:1–3

# 41. Magnificent Warrior

Josh 5:13-15;
Ps 93:1; 45:3-5; 149:6-9

Graham Kendrick

2. Magnificent Warrior,
   We hear Your strong command
   To join the ranks of light
   And march into the fight;
   By faith to overthrow
   Ten thousand Jerichos,
   To make Your judgements known
   In all the earth.

# 42.

# May the fragrance

2 Cor 2:14; 3:18; Eph 5:2

Graham Kendrick

2. May the glory of Jesus fill His church. (*men*)
   May the glory of Jesus fill His church. (*ladies*)
   May the glory of Jesus fill His church. (*men*)
   Radiant glory of Jesus, (*ladies*)
   Shining from our faces ⎫
   As we gaze in adoration.⎭ (*all*)

3. May the beauty of Jesus fill my life. (*men*)
   May the beauty of Jesus fill my life. (*ladies*)
   May the beauty of Jesus fill my life. (*men*)
   Perfect beauty of Jesus, (*ladies*)
   Fill my thoughts my words my deeds ⎫
   My all I give in adoration. ⎭ (*All — twice.*)

―――――― ♦♦♦ ――――――

*Shout for joy to the Lord, all the*
    *earth,*
    *burst into jubilant song with*
    *music;*
*make music to the Lord with the*
    *harp,*
    *with the harp and the sound of*
    *singing,*
*with trumpets and the blast of the*
    *ram's horn –*
    *shout for joy before the Lord, the*
    *King.*

PSALM 98:4–6

―――――― ♦♦♦ ――――――

# 43.

# Meekness and majesty
## (This is your God)

Mt 11:29; Lk 23:34;
Jn 13:5; Phil 2:6–9

Graham Kendrick

Bow down and wor-ship ———— for this is your God, ———— this is your God. ———— God, ———— this is your God. ————

2. Father's pure radiance,
   Perfect in innocence,
   Yet learns obedience
   To death on a cross.
   Suffering to give us life,
   Conquering through sacrifice,
   And as they crucify
   Prays: "Father forgive."

3. Wisdom unsearchable,
   God the invisible,
   Love indestructable
   In frailty appears.
   Lord of infinity,
   Stooping so tenderly,
   Lifts our humanity
   To the heights of His throne.

**44.**

# My heart is full
## (All the glory)

Ps 45:1, 4, 6–8; Heb 1:8–9;
Rev 4:11; 5:12

Graham Kendrick

Moderately

1. *(Men)* My heart is full of ad - mir - a - tion

for You, my Lord, my God and King.

*(All)* Your ex - cel - lence, my in - spi - ra - tion,

Your words of grace have made my spi - rit sing.

All __ the glo - ry, hon - our and

2. You love what's right and hate what's evil,  *(Men)*
   Therefore Your God sets You on high,
   And on Your head pours oil of gladness,  *(Women)*
   While fragrance fills Your royal palaces.

3. Your throne, O God, will last forever,  *(All)*
   Justice will be Your royal decree.
   In majesty, ride out victorious,
   For righteousness, truth and humility.

# 45. My Lord, what love is this
## (Amazing love)

Is 53:3; Rom 5:8; Eph 5:2

Graham Kendrick

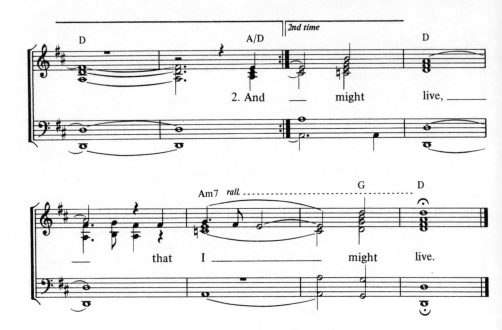

2. And so they watched Him die,
   Despised, rejected;
   But oh, the blood He shed
   Flowed for me!

3. And now this love of Christ
   Shall flow like rivers;
   Come wash your guilt away,
   Live again!

*Enter his gates with thanksgiving
and his courts with praise;
give thanks to him and praise his
name.*

PSALM 100:4

# 46. Now dawns the Sun of righteousness
## (Tell out, tell out the news)

Graham Kendrick

**Joyful and bright**

*Verse*

1. Now dawns the Sun of _ right - eous-ness, and the dark-ness will ne-ver His bright-ness dim; true light that lights the _ hearts of men, on-ly Son of the Fa-ther, Je - sus Christ. _____ Tell

*Chorus*

out, tell out _ the _ news, on ev - 'ry street pro-claim a _ Child is born, a Son is giv'n, and Je - sus is His name! Tell

out, tell out __ the __ news, our Sa-viour Christ has come, in __ ev-'ry tribe and na - tion let songs of praise be sung, let songs of praise be sung!

D.C. | Last time only

2. Laughter and joy He will increase,
   All our burdens be lifted,
   Oppression cease;
   The blood-stained battle-dress be burned,
   And the art of our warfare
   Never more be learned.

3. So let us go, His witnesses,
   Spreading news of His kingdom
   Of righteousness,
   'Till the whole world has heard the song,
   'Till the harvest is gathered,
   Then the end shall come.

# 47.

# O, heaven is in my heart
## (Heaven is in my heart)

*Ps 16:11; Lk 17:20;*
*1 Cor 3:11; Eph 2:20–22;*
*1 Thess 4:16; Heb 10:19;*
*Rev 22:17*

Graham Kendrick

2. His precious life on me He spent.                    *(All)*
   Heaven is in my heart.
   To give me life without an end,
   Heaven is in my heart.
   In Christ is all my confidence,
   Heaven is in my heart.
   The hope of my inheritance,
   Heaven is in my heart.

3. We are a temple for His throne,          *(Women)*
   Heaven is in my heart.                   *(All)*
   And Christ is the foundation stone,      *(Women)*
   Heaven is in my heart.                   *(All)*
   He will return to take us home,          *(Women)*
   Heaven is in my heart.                   *(All)*
   The Spirit and the Bride say "Come!"     *(Women)*
   Heaven is in my heart.                   *(All)*

# 48.    O Lord, the clouds are gathering

*Lam 4:4;*
*Amos 5:24;*
*Mt 6:10; Lk 11:2*

*N.B. Some congregations may find this song more comfortable to sing in a slightly lower key, e.g. B major.*

Graham Kendrick

2. O Lord, over the nations now
   Where is the dove of peace?
   Her wings are broken.
   O Lord, while precious children starve
   The tools of war increase;
   Their bread is stolen.

3. O Lord, dark powers are poised to flood
   Our streets with hate and fear;
   We must awaken!
   O Lord, let love reclaim the lives
   That sin would sweep away
   And let Your kingdom come.

4. Yet, O Lord, Your glorious cross shall tower
   Triumphant in this land,
   Evil confounding.
   Through the fire Your suffering church display
   The glories of her Christ:
   Praises resounding!

# 49.

# O Lord, Your tenderness

*Ps 51:1–2; Jas 5:11*

Graham Kendrick

# 50.

# One shall tell another
## (The wine of the kingdom)

*Joel 1:3; Mt 5:16; 9:17;*
*Mk 2:22; Lk 5:37; Jn 2:10;*
*Acts 2:46–47*

**Lightly with increasing pace**

Graham Kendrick

1. One shall tell a - noth - er, and he shall tell his friend, hus - bands, wives and chil - dren shall come fol - low - ing on. From house to house in fam - i - lies shall more be gath - ered in, and lights will shine in ev'-ry street, so warm and welcom - ing.

**Chorus**

Come on in and taste the new wine, the wine of the

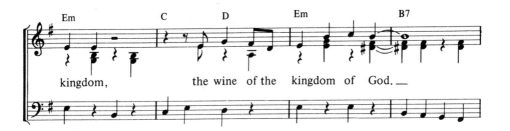

kingdom, the wine of the kingdom of God. __

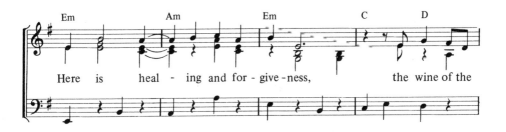

Here is heal - ing and for - give - ness, the wine of the

*D.S. ( ℅ )*
*Last time*
*then end*

kingdom, the wine of the kingdom of God. _____

*Last time only*
Em

2. Compassion of the Father
   Is ready now to flow,
   Through acts of love and mercy
   We must let it show.
   He turns now from His anger
   To show a smiling face
   And longs that men should stand beneath
   The fountain of His grace.

3. He longs to do much more than
   Our faith has yet allowed,
   To thrill us and surprise us
   With His sovereign power.
   Where darkness has been darkest
   The brightest light will shine,
   His invitation comes to us,
   It's yours and it is mine.

# 51.
# O what a mystery I see

Graham Kendrick

1. O what a mystery I see, what marvelous design, that God should come as one of us, a Son in David's line. Flesh of our flesh, of woman born, our humanness He owns; and for a world of wickedness His

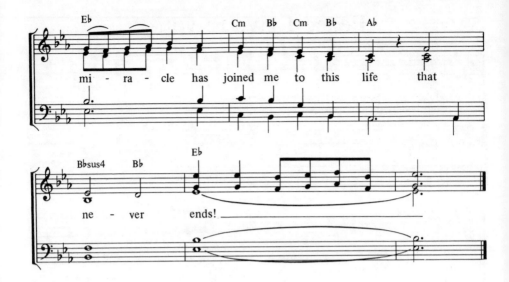

mi - ra - cle has joined me to this life that ne - ver ends!

2. This perfect Man, incarnate God,
   By selfless sacrifice
   Destroyed our sinful history,
   All fallen Adam's curse.
   In Him the curse to blessing turns,
   My barren spirit flowers,
   As over the shattered power of sin
   The cross of Jesus towers.

3. By faith a child of His I stand,
   An heir in David's line,                  *(Women)*
   Royal descendant by His blood
   Destined by Love's design.
   Fathers of faith, my fathers now! *(Men)*
   Because in Christ I am,
   And all God's promises in Him      *(All)*
   To me are 'Yes, Amen'!

4. No more then as a child of earth
   Must I my lifetime spend —
   His history, His destiny
   Are mine to apprehend.
   Oh what a Saviour, what a Lord,
   O Master, Brother, Friend!
   What miracle has joined me to
   This life that never ends!

# 52.

# Peace I give to you

Jn 14:27; 2 Cor 1:3-4

Graham Kendrick

1. Peace I give to you, I give to you My peace.

peace. Let it flow to one a - no - ther, let it

flow, let it flow. Let it flow.

2.  Love I give to you. . . (etc.)

3.  Hope. . . (etc.)

4.  Joy. . . (etc.)

5.  Grace. . . (etc.)

6.  Power. . . (etc.)

———————— ♦♦♦ ————————

*In the beginning you laid the
    foundations of the earth,
  and the heavens are the work of your
    hands.
They will perish, but you remain;
  they will all wear out like a
    garment.
Like clothing you will change them
  and they will be discarded.
But you remain the same,
  and your years will never end.*

PSALM 102:25–27

———————— ♦♦♦ ————————

# 53.

# Peace to you

*Is 9:6; Jn 14:27; 20:19*

Graham Kendrick

# 54.

# Praise to our God

2 Chron 5:13-14

Capo 5(Am)

Graham Kendrick

Praise to our God who a-lone is the migh - ty — One
Bring to Him now, as an of - f'ring a fra - grance sweet,

— rob'd in ma jes ty, come and bow down, wor - ship and a -
— all the pray-ers of your heart to His throne; with thanks-giv - ing

dore.
come.
The Lord Al-migh - ty,

— His love en-dures for ev - er, His

grace _____ and mer - cy ev - er sure. _____

_ His pow'r will ne - ver, _____ ne - ver fail or

fal - ter, or His love _____

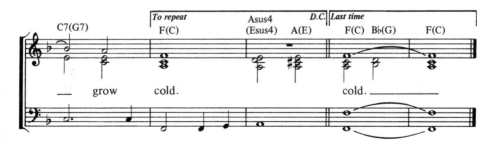

_ grow cold. cold. _____

# 55.
# Praise to the Lord

*Lam 3:22-23; Ps 148; 34:8*

Capo 3(D)

Graham Kendrick

Brightly

Bb(G)  C(A)  F(D)  Bb(G)  F(D)

*Verse*

1. Praise to the Lord! Sing Al - le - lu - ias
Praise to His name! Let ev - 'ry crea - ture

Gm(Em)  F(D)  *1st time* Bb(G)  Csus4 (Asus4)  C(A)

to the __ King of all the __ earth.
join in the joy - ful

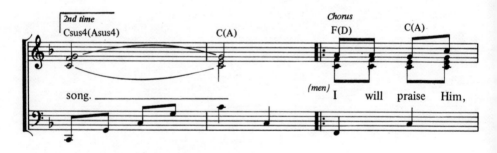

*2nd time* Csus4(Asus4)  C(A)  *Chorus* F(D)  C(A)

song. _____

*(men)* I will praise Him,

F(D)  C(A)  Dm(Bm)  G(E)  Dm(Bm)  G(E)

*(women)* (I will praise Him,)  *(men)* I will ex-alt Him  *(women)* (I will ex - alt Him)

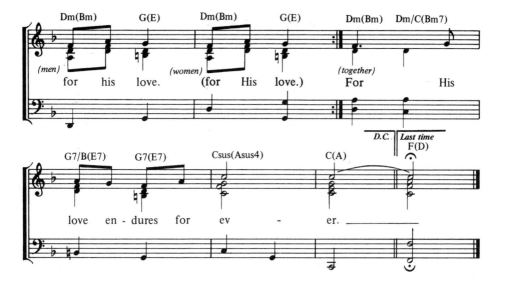

2. Praise to the Lord!
   The wind and the waves,
   The thunder and rain,
   Display His power.
   Raise now the shout!
   Come lift up your voice
   And join with all nature's song.

3. Praise to the Lord!
   O taste and see
   His goodness and mercy
   Never fail.
   Praise to His name!
   Who gives to His children
   Gifts from His generous hand.

# 56. Rejoice!

Josh 6:2, 7; Ezek 37:10; Mt 21:7; Mk 11:7;
Lk 19:35–36; Jn 12:14; 1 Cor 4:20; 2 Cor 4:7;
12:10; Col 1:27; Rev 19:11

Graham Kendrick

Re-joice! Re-joice! Christ is in you, the hope of glo-ry in our hearts. He lives! He lives! His breath is in you, a-rise a migh-ty ar-my, we a-rise.

1. Now is the time for us to march u-pon the land, in-to our

hands He will give the ground _ we claim. _____

A                                      Bm

He rides in ma-jes-ty _ to lead us in - to vic - to-ry,_

G          Bm          Em7      Asus4   A

the world shall see that Christ is Lord! _____ Re -

2. God is at work in us
   His purpose to perform,
   Building a kingdom
   Of power not of words,
   Where things impossible
   By faith shall be made possible;
   Let's give the glory
   To Him now.

3. Though we are weak, His grace
   Is everything we need;
   We're made of clay
   But this treasure is within.
   He turns our weaknesses
   Into His opportunities,
   So that the glory
   Goes to Him.

# 57.

# Restore, O Lord

*Ps 23:4; 85:4; 102:27; 136:1; Hab 3:2, 6;*
*1 Cor 3:13; Heb 1:12; 3:12; Rev 11:15*

Graham Kendrick/Chris Rolinson

Steadily with feeling

1. Re - store, O Lord, the hon-our of Your name, in
4.

works of sov'reign pow - er come shake the earth a - gain, that

men may see and come with rev'-rent fear to the liv - ing God_

_ whose king-dom shall _ out - last the years. _____

2. Restore, O Lord,
   In all the earth Your fame,
   And in our time revive
   The church that bears Your name.
   And in Your anger,
   Lord, remember mercy,
   O living God
   Whose mercy shall outlast the years.

3. Bend us, O Lord,
   Where we are hard and cold,
   In Your refiner's fire
   Come purify the gold.
   Though suffering comes
   And evil crouches near,
   Still our living God
   Is reigning, He is reigning here.

4. *As verse 1*

# 58. Save, save, save

*Deut 4;24; Neh 1:5-11; Ez 22:30*

Graham Kendrick

**Reverently**

1. Save, save, save the peo-ple of this land, O Lord, for You, You are a God of mer - cy. fire.

*To repeat*

*To end*

2. Send, send, send
   The fire of Your Spirit, Lord,
   For O, our God is a consuming fire.

# 59.
## Show Your power, O Lord

Capo 2(G)

Ps 68:28, 35

Graham Kendrick

1. Show Your power O Lord, demon-strate the just-ice of Your king-dom. Prove Your might-y word, vin-di-cate Your name before a watch-ing world. Awe-some are Your deeds, O

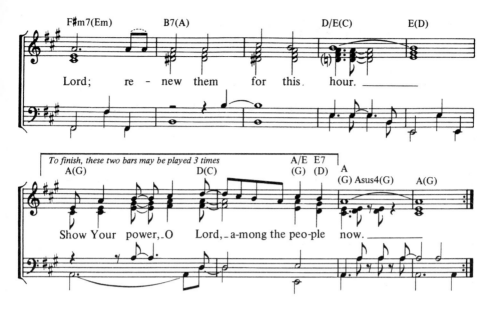

2. Show Your power, O Lord,
   Cause Your church to rise and take action.
   Let all fear be gone,
   Powers of the age to come
   Are breaking through.
   We Your people are ready to serve,
   To arise and to obey.
   Show Your power, O Lord,
   And set the people free.

   *Ending last time*
   Show Your power, O Lord,
   And set the people —
   Show Your power, O Lord,
   And set the people —
   Show Your power, O Lord,
   And set the people free.

# 60.  Soften my heart, Lord

*Ezek 11:19; 36:26*

Graham Kendrick

# 61. Such love

Jn 3:16

Capo 4(C)

Graham Kendrick

**Flowing**

1. Such love, _____ pure as the whit - est snow; _____ such love _____ weeps for the shame I know; _____ such love, _____ pay-ing the debt I owe; _____ O Je - sus, _____ such love. _____

2. Such love, stilling my restlessness;
   Such love, filling my emptiness;
   Such love, showing me holiness;
   O Jesus, such love.

3. Such love springs from eternity;
   Such love, streaming through history;
   Such love, fountain of life to me;
   O Jesus, such love.

# 62.

# Thank You for the cross
## (Oh I love You, Lord)

Ps 18:19; Is 42:1;
Zeph 3:17; Col 1:14;
Heb 7:25; 1 Pet 2:24

Capo 3(G)

Graham Kendrick

**Quietly**

*Verse*

1. Thank You for the cross, the price You paid for us, how You
   Now our sins are gone, all for - giv - en, cov-er'd

gave Your-self so com-plete-ly, pre-cious Lord. (Pre-cious Lord.) Oh I
by Your blood, all for - got - ten, thank You Lord. (Thank You Lord.)

*(Women)*

**Brightly**
*Chorus*

love You, Lord, real-ly love You, Lord. I will ne-ver un-der-stand why You love

me. You're my deep-est joy, — You're my heart's de-light, — and the

great-est thing of all, O Lord, I see: You de-light in me!

2.  For our healing there        Calvary's work is done,
    Lord You suffered,          You have conquered,
    And to take our fear        Able now to save
    You poured out Your love,   So completely,
    Precious Lord. (Precious Lord.)  Thank You Lord. (Thank You Lord.)

# 63.

# The King is among us

*Zeph 3:17; Mt 18:20;*
*Acts 1:4; 1 Cor 12:11*

Graham Kendrick

1. The King is a-mong us, His
7.
Spi-rit is here, _____ let's draw near and wor — ship, let songs fill the air. _____

*1-6*
*Last time only*
2. He

2. He looks down upon us,
   Delight in His face,
   Enjoying His children's love,
   Enthralled by our praise.

3. For each child is special,
   Accepted and loved,
   A love gift from Jesus
   To His Father above.

4. And now He is giving
   His gifts to us all,
   For no one is worthless
   And each one is called.

5. The Spirit's anointing
   On all flesh comes down,
   And we shall be channels
   For works like His own.

6. We come now believing
   Your promise of power,
   For we are Your people
   And this is Your hour.

7. *As verse 1*

# 64.

# The Lord is King

*Ex 15:3,7,6,2*

Capo 4 (C)

Graham Kendrick

The Lord is King, He is migh - ty in bat - tle,
Lord is King, so ma - jest - ic in pow - er,

work - ing won - ders;          glor - ious in
His right hand has          shat - tered the

ma - jes - ty.                    The
en - e

*(Part one)* This is my God

- my.

# 65.

# The Lord is marching out

## (O give thanks)

Ps 136:1; Rev 19:11

Graham Kendrick

Capo 2 (Am)

**March**
*Verse*

1. The Lord is mar-ching out in splen-dour,
in awe-some ma - jes-ty He rides,
for truth, hu - mil - i - ty and just - ice,
His migh - ty ar - my fills the skies.

*Chorus*

O give thanks to the Lord __ for His love en - dures, O give

2. His army marches out with dancing
   For He has filled our hearts with joy.
   Be glad the kingdom is advancing,
   The love of God, our battle cry!

# 66.

# The price is paid

Is 53:4–5; Mt 28:18; Rom 8:1;
16:20; 1 Cor 7:23; Col 2:15;
1 Pet 2:24; Rev 5:9

Graham Kendrick

Triumphantly

1. The price is paid, come let us en-ter in to all that Je-sus died to make our own. For ev-'ry sin more than e-nough He gave, and bought our free-dom from each guil-ty stain. The price is paid, A-lle-lu-ia, a-maz-ing grace, so strong and sure and so with all my heart,— my life in

ev-'ry __ part, __ I live to thank You for __ the price You paid. __

The price is

paid.

2.  The price is paid,
    See Satan flee away;
    For Jesus crucified
    Destroys his power.
    No more to pay,
    Let accusation cease,
    In Christ there is
    No condemnation now.

3.  The price is paid,
    And by that scourging cruel
    He took our sicknesses
    As if His own.
    And by His wounds
    His body broken there,
    His healing touch may now
    By faith be known.

4.  The price is paid,
    'Worthy the Lamb' we cry,
    Eternity shall never
    Cease His praise.
    The Church of Christ
    Shall rule upon the earth,
    In Jesus' name we have
    Authority.

# 67. There's a sound on the wind
## (Battle hymn)

Phil 2:10;
1 Thess 4:16;
Rev 4:4; 7:14; 21:4

Graham Kendrick

*Triumphantly*

1. There's a sound on the wind like a vic-tor-y song, lis-ten now, let it rest on your soul. It's a song that I learn'd from a heav-en-ly King, it's the song of a bat - tle royal.

*1st and 3rd time* royal.
*2nd and 4th times* sing. / fly!
*To refrain*

2. There's a loud shout of victory that leaps from our hearts
   As we wait for our conquering King.
   There's a triumph resounding from dark ages past
   To the victory song we now sing.

   *Refrain*

3. There'll be crowns for the conquerors and white robes to wear,
   There will be no more sorrow or pain.
   And the battles of earth shall be lost in the sight
   Of the glorious Lamb that was slain.

4. Now the King of the ages approaches the earth,
   He will burst through the gates of the sky.
   And all men shall bow down to His beautiful name;
   We shall rise with a shout, we shall fly!

   *Refrain*

5. *As verse 4.*

# 68.

# The trumpets sound
## (The feast is ready)

Ps 23:5; Mt 22:2; Lk 1:53; 14:17

Graham Kendrick

In a 'fiesta' style (♩ = 153)

(Leader speaks:) In Jesus, God has prepared a feast of good things for all who will accept His invitation. Come on: the feast is ready!

1. The trumpets sound, the an - gels sing, the feast is rea - dy to be-gin; the gates of heav'n are op - en wide, and Je - sus

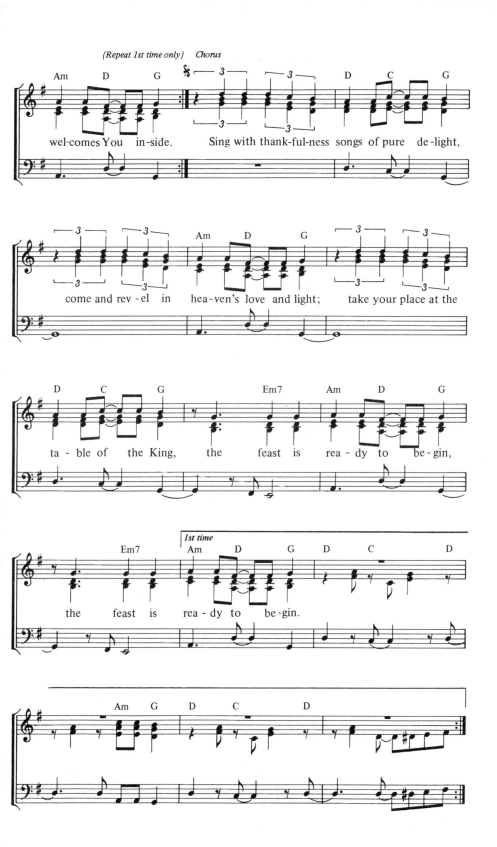

2. Tables are laden with good things,
   O taste the peace and joy He brings;
   He'll fill you up with love divine,
   He'll turn your water into wine.

3. The hungry heart He satisfies,
   Offers the poor His paradise;
   Now hear all heaven and earth applaud
   The amazing goodness of the Lord.

———————— ♦♦♦ ————————

*Praise the Lord, you his angels,*
*you mighty ones who do his*
*bidding,*
*who obey his word.*
*Praise the Lord, all his heavenly*
*hosts,*
*you his servants who do his will.*
*Praise the Lord, all his works*
*everywhere in his dominion.*

PSALM 103:20–22

———————— ♦♦♦ ————————

# 69.
# This is My belovèd Son
## (That the Lamb who was slain)

Lk 3:22; Jn 3:16-17;
Mt 9:37-38; 28:19;
Rev 5:12; 19:7-9

Graham Kendrick

Capo 2(Em)

1. This is My be - lov-èd Son who tast-ed death that you, My child, might live. See the blood He shed for you, what suf-fer - ing, say what more could He give? Cloth'd in His per-fec - tion bring praise, a fra-grance sweet,

gar-land-ed with joy, come wor-ship at His feet, that the Lamb who was slain might re- ceive the re- ward, might re- ceive the re- ward of His suf-fer- ing.

2. Look, the world's great harvest fields
   Are ready now
   And Christ commands us: 'Go!'
   Countless souls are dying
   So hopelessly,
   His wond'rous love unknown.
   Lord, give us the nations
   For the glory of the King.
   Father send more labourers
   The lost to gather in.

3. Come the day when we will stand
   There face to face,
   What joy will fill His eyes.
   For at last His bride appears
   So beautiful,
   Her glory fills the skies.
   Drawn from every nation,
   People, tribe and tongue;
   All creation sings,
   The wedding has begun.

   *And the Lamb who was slain shall receive the reward,*
   *Shall receive the reward of His suffering.*

# 70. To keep Your lovely face

*Ps 27:4,8; 34:5*

Capo 2 (D)

Graham Kendrick

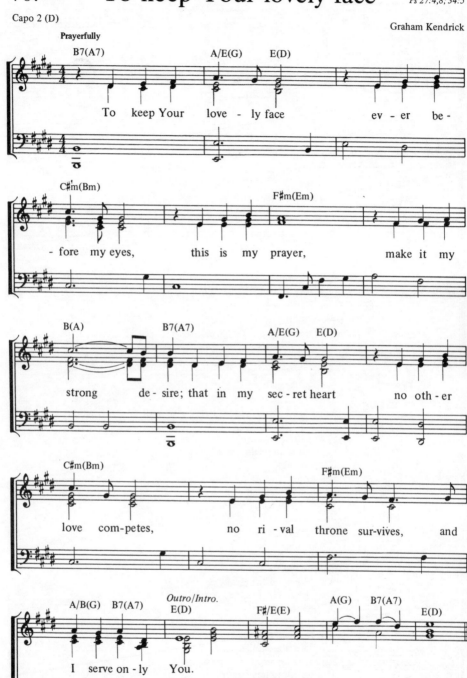

To keep Your love - ly face ev - er be - fore my eyes, this is my prayer, make it my strong de - sire; that in my sec - ret heart no oth - er love com-petes, no ri - val throne sur-vives, and I serve on - ly You.

# 71.
# We are here to praise You

*Rom 8:15; Gal 4:6;*
*Heb 13:15*

Capo 2(D)

Graham Kendrick

We are here to praise You,
lift our hearts and sing.

We are here to give You
the best that we can bring.

And it is our love
give You
rising from our hearts,
pleasure and de - light,

ev'ry-thing with-in us cries:
heart and mind and will that say:
*1st time*
'Ab - ba Fa-ther.'

*2nd time*
Help us now to
'I love You Lord.'

# 72.

# We are His children
## (Go forth in His name)

Graham Kendrick

**With life**

1. We are His child-ren, the fruit of His suff-'ring, saved and re-deemed by His blood; called to be ho-ly, a light to the na-tions: clothed with his power, ____ filled with His love. ____

**Chorus**

Go forth in His name, pro-claim-ing 'Je-sus reigns!'

Now is the time — for the church to a-rise and pro-claim Him, 'Je-sus,

Sa-viour, Re-deem-er and Lord'. _____

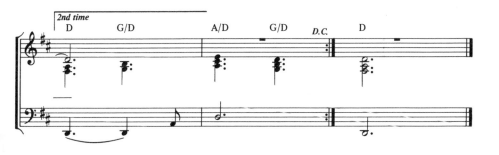

2. Countless the souls that are stumbling in darkness;
   Why do we sleep in the light?
   Jesus commands us to go make disciples,
   This is our cause,
   This is our fight.

3. Listen, the wind of the Spirit is blowing,
   The end of the age is so near;
   Powers in the earth and the heavens are shaking,
   Jesus our Lord
   Soon shall appear!

## 73.

# We believe

Is 7:14; Lk 1:34–35; 1 Cor 15:3–4;
Phil 2:10–11; 1 Thess 4:16; Heb 1:3

Capo 2 (Em)

Graham Kendrick

**With strength**

F#m(Em)   E(D) F#m(Em)   E(D) F#m(Em)   Esus4 (Dsus4)   E(D)   F#m(Em)   E(D) F#m(Em)   E(D)

1. We be-lieve in God the Fa-ther, ma - ker of the

F#m(Em)   E(D)   F#m(Em)   E(D) F#m(Em)   E(D)   F#m(Em)   Esus4 (Dsus4)   E(D)

u - ni - verse, and in Christ His Son our Sa - viour,

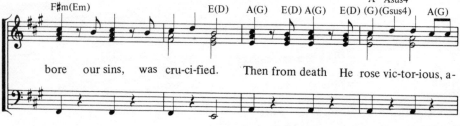

E   F#m
F#m(Em) (D)(Em)   E(D) F#m(Em)   E(D)   A(G)   E(D) A(G)   E(D)(G)   A Asus4 (Gsus4)   A(G)

come to us by vir - gin birth. We be-lieve He died to save us,

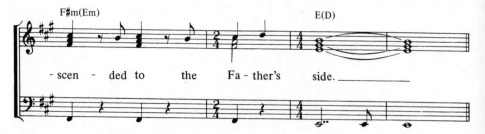

F#m(Em)   E(D)   A(G)   E(D) A(G)   E(D)(G)   A Asus4 (Gsus4)   A(G)

bore our sins, was cru-ci-fied. Then from death He rose vic-tor-ious, a-

F#m(Em)   E(D)

- scen - ded to the Fa - ther's side. _____

2. We believe He sends His Spirit,
   On His church with gifts of power.
   God His word of truth affirming,
   Sends us to the nations now.
   He will come again in glory,
   Judge the living and the dead.
   Every knee shall bow before Him,
   Then must every tongue confess.

## 74. We'll walk the land
### (Let the flame burn brighter)

*Mt 5:16*

Graham Kendrick

Capo 3 (D)

**With a strong rhythm**

1. We'll walk the land with hearts on fire; and ev-'ry

step will be a prayer. Hope is ris-ing, new day

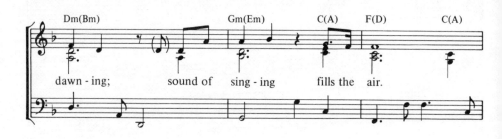

dawn-ing; sound of sing-ing fills the air.

2. Two thou-sand / Let the flame burn

2. Two thousand years, and still the flame
   Is burning bright across the land.
   Hearts are waiting, longing, aching,
   For awakening once again.

3. We'll walk for truth, speak out for love;
   In Jesus' name we shall be strong,
   To lift the fallen, to save the children,
   To fill the nation with Your song.

*Let the name of the Lord be praised*
*both now and for evermore.*
*From the rising of the sun to the*
*place where it sets*
*the name of the Lord is to be*
*praised.*

PSALM 113:2–3

# 75.  We shall stand

*Is 50:7; Lk 9:51; Jn 15:16; 2 Cor 3:18; Eph 6:13; Rev 22:4*

Capo 3(D)

Graham Kendrick

Lyrics:

We shall stand, with our feet on the Rock. What-ev-er men may say we'll lift Your name up high. And we shall walk through the dark-est night; set-ting our fa-ces like flint we'll walk in-to the light.

*Verse*

1. Lord You have cho - sen me _ for _ fruit - ful - ness, _____ to be trans-formed _ in - to _ Your _ like ness. _____ I'm gon-na fight on through _ 'till I see You _ face _ _ to _ face. _

♦ CODA

2. Lord as Your witnesses
   You've appointed us.
   And with Your Holy Spirit
   Anointed us.
   And so I'll fight on through
   'Till I see You face to face.

# 76. We will cross every border
## (Cross every border)

Graham Kendrick

Fairly slow, with strength

1. We will cross _____ ev'ry bor - der, throw wide _____ ev'ry door, join-ing our hands _____ a-cross the na-tions, we'll pro-claim Je-sus is Lord. Lord. Then we'll pro-claim Je-sus is Lord. We shall pro-claim Je-sus is Lord.

2. We will break sin's oppression,
   Speak out for the poor,
   Announce the coming of Christ's kingdom,
   From east to west and shore to shore.

3. We will gather in the harvest,
   And work while it's day,
   Though we may sow with tears of sadness,
   We will reap with shouts of joy.

4. Soon our eyes shall see His glory,
   The Lamb, our risen Lord,
   When He receives from every nation
   His blood-bought Bride, His great reward.
   Then we'll proclaim Jesus is Lord.
   We shall proclaim Jesus is Lord.

*Praise God in his sanctuary;*
*praise him in his mighty heavens.*
*Praise him for his acts of power;*
*praise him for his surpassing*
*greatness.*

PSALM 150:1–2

# 77. Who can sound the depths of sorrow

Capo 1(A)

*Lev 18:21; Ps 85:4–7; Is 53:3; Jer 32:35; 1 Jn 1:7*

With feeling

Graham Kendrick

1. Who can sound the depths of sor-row in the Fa-ther heart of God, for the child-ren we've re-ject-ed, for the lives so deep-ly scarred? And each light that we've ex-tin-guished has brought dark-ness to our land: u-pon our na-tion, u-pon our na-tion have

mer - cy,   Lord.       Lord._____

2. We have scorned the truth You gave us,
   We have bowed to other lords.
   We have sacrificed the children
   On the altars of our gods.
   O let truth again shine on us,
   Let Your holy fear descend:
   Upon our nation, upon our nation
   Have mercy Lord.

   *(Men)*
3. Who can stand before Your anger?
   Who can face Your piercing eyes?
   For You love the weak and helpless,
   And You hear the victims' cries.
   *(All)*
   Yes, You are a God of justice,
   And Your judgement surely comes:
   Upon our nation, upon our nation
   Have mercy, Lord.

   *(Women)*
4. Who will stand against the violence?
   Who will comfort those who mourn?
   In an age of cruel rejection,
   Who will build for love a home?
   *(All)*
   Come and shake us into action,
   Come and melt our hearts of stone:
   Upon Your people, upon Your people
   Have mercy, Lord.

5. Who can sound the depths of mercy
   In the Father heart of God?
   For there is a Man of sorrows
   Who for sinners shed His blood.
   He can heal the wounds of nations,
   He can wash the guilty clean:
   Because of Jesus, because of Jesus
   Have mercy, Lord.

*N.B. Some congregations may wish to add to the effectiveness of this song
by transposing the final verse up a semitone, into B major.*

# 78. With my whole heart

Song 5:10; Rev 22:17

Graham Kendrick

*Joyfully with swing*

1. With my whole heart I will praise You, hold-ing no-thing back, Hal - le - lu - jah! You have made me glad and now I come with op - en arms to thank You, with my heart em - brace, Hal - le - lu - jah! I can see Your

2. Lord, Your heart is overflowing
   With a love divine, Hallelujah!
   And this love is mine for ever.
   Now Your joy has set You laughing
   As You join the song, Hallelujah!
   Heaven sings along, I hear the
   Voices swell to great crescendos,
   Praising Your great love, Hallelujah!
   O amazing love! O amazing love!

3. Come, O Bridegroom, clothed in splendour,
   My Beloved One, Hallelujah!
   How I long to run and meet You.
   You're the fairest of ten thousand,
   You're my life and breath, Hallelujah!
   Love as strong as death has won me.
   All the rivers, all the oceans
   Cannot quench this love, Hallelujah!
   O amazing love! O amazing love!

# INDEX

In this index, titles where different from first lines are shown in *italics*.

# Graham Kendrick
# MAKE WAY
## Series

These products will provide an essential resource for all those considering 'Make Way' style events, both on and off of the streets.

**MAKE WAY FOR THE
KING - A CARNIVAL
OF PRAISE**
cassette (MWC1)

**MAKE WAY FOR JESUS
- SHINE, JESUS, SHINE**
cassette (MWC2
compact disc (MWD2

**MAKE WAY FOR
CHRISTMAS - THE GIFT**
cassette (MW3)
compact disc (MWD3)

**MAKE WAY FOR THE
CROSS -
LET THE FLAME BURN
BRIGHTER**
cassette (MWC4
compact disc (MWD4

**MAKE WAY -
MARCH FOR JESUS -
CROWN HIM**
cassette (MWC005)
compact disc (MWD005)
songbook

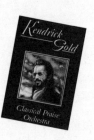

**KENDRICK GOLD**
A selection of
Graham Kendrick's
most popular songs set to
a full orchestral
arrangement.
KMC576
KMCD576

**MAKE WAY SONGBOOK - PUBLIC PRAISE**
Handbook and street songs from:
Shine, Jesus, Shine, A Carnival of Praise, The Gift, The Cross

Also by Graham Kendrick
**WORSHIP** (paperback)
Whether you are a leader of worship or see yourself as playing a more passive role, this book is designed to help you experience greater depth and meaning in your highest calling - to worship the living God.

Order from your local Christian Bookshop or in case of difficulty, direct from The Rainbow Company, 1 St Anne's Road, Eastbourne, East Sussex, BN21 3UN

# *Songs of Fellowship Resources*

## SONGS OF FELLOWSHIP ACETATES

Are you tired of trying to read the handwritten scrawl that appears on the screen?

Like to pick and choose the songs that your church uses?

Then you need this Songs of Fellowship Worship resource.

Enquiries to:
Songs of Fellowship Acetate Service, 55 Bridge Road, Chertsey, Surrey, KT16 8JR.
Tel: 0932 565614

---

## SONGS OF FELLOWSHIP ARRANGEMENT SERVICE

Apart from the fully scored music editions, individual instrumental and vocal arrangements are available for most of the songs in the Songs of Fellowship range from:

The Songs of Fellowship Arrangement Service,
PO Box 4, Sheffield, South Yorkshire D1 1DU.

Please send an A4 stamped addressed envelope (100 grammes postage) for song list and prices.
Please state what vocal or instrumental arrangements you are interested in.

---

Keep up to date with the best new worship songs, using the convenient THANKYOU MUSIC UPDATE - drawn from the resources of Britain's leading worship publisher. Savour the best new songs from Songs of Fellowship, and use them to enrich the life and witness of your church.

THANKYOU MUSIC UPDATE has several helpful features which will help you as a worship leader or musician.

✳  6 new songs - every three months.

✳  A professionally recorded cassette containing a musical and vocal version of each song.

✳  A 'backing track' version of the song on the same cassette. This can help the worship group and the church learn the song. You can also use it in situations where you might not have musicians readily available, such as housegroups.

✳  Fully scored sheet music for every song.

✳  A helpful teaching article on an aspect of worship.

Songs from the leading Worship Leaders of Britain and America plus other new song writers.

**Available from: Thankyou Music, 1 St Anne's Road, Eastbourne, East Sussex BN21 3UN**